ALL UPON A STONE

BY JEAN CRAIGHEAD GEORGE
Illustrated by Don Bolognese

ALL UPON A STONE

Thomas Y. Crowell Company, New York

Manufactured in the United States of America

L.C. Card 75-101929

ISBN 0-690-05532-3
      0-690-05533-1 (Lib. Ed.)

1   2   3   4   5   6   7   8   9   10

ALL UPON A STONE

Each of the illustrations in this book is a detail of a single painting reproduced at the end of the book, an unusual pictorial technique chosen by the artist to reflect the unity of the microcosm of the stone. The painting was executed in acrylics on canvas and measures three feet by four feet. The individual illustrations can be found in the master painting.

In the woods by a stream lies an old worn stone. It is big as a bear and gray as a rain cloud.

Moss gardens grow on its ridges and humps. Ferns cast shadows of lace on its sides. A puddle of water lies like a lake near its top and butterflies sit nearby.

A stone by a stream in the woods is like a tiny country. It has its own forests, valleys, and pools. It has its own creatures that live out their lives, hunting, sleeping, and working all upon a stone.

A summer day dawns.

Deep under the stone a mole cricket moves.

Fuzzy hairs cover his back like fur. His feet are small shovels that dig the soil as he hunts for food.

As he works by himself in the ground under the stone, he breathes through his belly. He hears with his knees, smells with his antennae, and sees through the thousands of parts of his eyes.

Since his hatching in spring his knees have never heard another mole cricket. His antennae have never smelled one.

Now on this summer day his antennae stretched as he sniffed for the scent of another mole cricket. He peered around roots looking for furry backs, shovels, and knees just like his own.

Tunneling as he searched, he worked himself up to the bottom of the stone.

There he came to a sowbug. He gently touched her with his antenna, but she was no mole cricket. She tucked down her head, pulled in her feet, and rolled herself into a ball.

He crept a little farther, lifting his
knees to listen for the crackles of a
mole cricket.

He met a ground beetle. She clicked.
He went on.

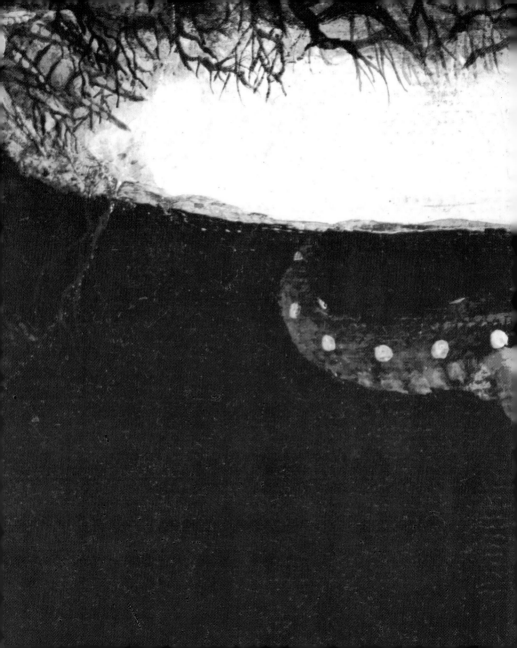

With his shovels he dug up a sala-
mander that was lying under the stone.
Its back was not furry but slick and wet.

With his knees he listened to spiders,
centipedes, and ants, but he heard no
mole cricket crackles.

He tunneled to the surface and came up beside the edge of the stone.

Thousands of sunbeams spun in his eyes. To shade them he pushed his head between his brown shovels. His two big eyes protected, he entered a path that led up through the moss that covered one side of the stone.

Slowly he climbed.

He heard silken slithers. He followed the sound through the moss. A wood snail was sliding on its big foot. A bright path of silver marked where it had walked.

The mole cricket hurried along.

Under a fern he paused for a rest. A pleasant odor came down his antennae.

He peered through the thousands of parts of his eyes. It was only a firefly asleep in the fern fronds waiting for twilight, his hour to fly and to glow.

The cricket stepped along with all his six feet.

At the edge of a pit filled with stone dust he listened again.

He heard crashes, not crackles. Worker ants were stacking sand grains on sand grains. The sound was enormous.

At last he came to the pool in the stone. It smelled like a mole cricket.

He grew excited. He fell in. Plowing the water of the rock pool as if it were soil, he swam.

And as he swam he passed fairy shrimp. They darted away upside down for they live on their backs.

Young mosquitoes flipped to the bottom of the pool. His shovels struck algae and rotifers and fresh-water jelly-fish. He bumped the tip of a fresh-water sponge.

But he did not find a mole cricket.

He beached in a grove of bright bluets and dried off his fur with his second pair of legs.

Silver wings flashed. The mole cricket lifted his knees. The clatter of stone flies was all that he heard. They had hatched in the stream by the stone and were dancing above the bluet grove.

He wedged himself under a starflower.
A ground spider leaped to a leaf to
pounce on him. He scurried away.

Then in a jungle of liverwort plants the tap of his shovels on dry leaves and stone awakened a lizard. He sprang at the cricket. Terrified, the cricket dug himself into a hump of pincushion moss.

The lizard was baffled. He went back to his lair.

The mole cricket continued to dig, and soon came out in the sun. He saw that he had come to the top of the stone. It was scattered with lichens and smoothed by the rain.

He listened and looked.

No mole cricket crackles came to his knees. No furry backs glowed in the thousands of parts of his eyes.

He set up a wail. Locking one wing into the other, he sawed out his cry.

He crackled. He crackled his loneliness. He crackled his whereabouts. He crackled his need for other mole crickets.

Down on the stone dropped a single mole cricket. Speeding around trees came another. Up from the bank of the stream flew a third and a fourth, a fifth and a sixth and a seventh.

They gathered together as mole crickets do, not to mate, not to eat, but for reasons no one knows. Solitary creatures all the days of their lives, each leaves his earthen home on one festive night and rushes together with other mole crickets to dance, crackle, and touch.

The mole cricket joined them. His knees heard glorious crackles. He smelled the good scent of other mole crickets. He saw furry backs.

He mingled and met. He bumped, touched, and scrambled. He sang, whirled, and crackled. He danced all night to mole cricket sounds.

Then he sat still. He was weary. There were too many crackles, too many backs, too many knees, and too many eyes.

Wildly he flew from the stone. He crashed into other crickets flying away.

He zoomed to the ground and plunged into the loam. He tunneled and burrowed and scrambled toward silence. He dug away from the sight of mole cricket fur. He raced from the scent of their bodies.

He plowed to a quiet spot under the stone.

His senses now told him that he loved his mole cricket comforts deep in the earth, the silence, the darkness, the black hugging soil.

Back in his home he sighed through his belly, pulled down his antennae, and stretched out to rest under the stone.

ABOUT THE AUTHOR

The inspiration for *All Upon a Stone* came from Jean George's children, who when they were very small spent many hours in walks in the woods exploring the life under, around, and on stones. To young children, the tiny community seemed a whole world of just the proper size. Mrs. George is the author of many distinguished books for children, all of which have affirmed her remarkable sensitivity both to nature and to young people.

ABOUT THE ARTIST

Don Bolognese was born in New York and was graduated from the Cooper Union School of Art, where he now teaches. Mr. Bolognese is the illustrator of many children's books, among them *Washington's Birthday,* a Crowell Holiday Book, and Clyde Robert Bulla's *The Ghost of Windy Hill.*

Don Bolognese and his family live in Brooklyn, New York, but summer in Vermont where they enjoy their hobby—hunting wild mushrooms.